CHORAL CONNECTION

With A Little Help From My Friends

6 Beatles songs in close harmony

S.A.T.B.

Edited and arranged by: Peter Gritton

Here, There And Everywhere 3
John Lennon and Paul McCartney

Hey Jude 9
John Lennon and Paul McCartney

It's Only Love 15
John Lennon and Paul McCartney

Michelle 21
John Lennon and Paul McCartney

Penny Lane 28
John Lennon and Paul McCartney

With A Little Help From My Friends 38
John Lennon and Paul McCartney

Exclusive distributors:
Music Sales Limited,
Newmarket Road,
Bury St. Edmunds, Suffolk IP33 3YB.

ISBN 0.7119.2506.2
Order No. CH55986

Printed in the United Kingdom by
Caligraving Limited, Thetford, Norfolk.

CHESTER MUSIC
A division of Music Sales Limited
8/9 Frith Street, London W1V 5TZ.

CHESTER MUSIC

Foreword

In many ways, this collection of Beatles songs is more of a challenge than the Christmas volume by way of close harmony singing, but each voice part is individually tailored to provide maximum pleasure for the singers: the arranger has done his best to ensure that the essence of each song has not been obscured by the close-harmony medium, since the Beatles style is essentially ballad-like.

Arranger's Notes

1. **Breathing**. Wherever possible, stagger the breathing in longer phrases, unless the text and the music naturally allow for a breath. The will preserve the fluency, especially in the 'instrumental' background sounds like *ooh*, *ah* and *mm*. The sign ‿ below the text implies that no breath should be taken; sometimes this may contradict the punctuation. , above the stave indicates a breathing mark for all voices.

2. **Dynamics** have, on the whole, been layered in order to help bring out important melodic lines. Further dynamics may be added to give these lines more of a chance over the often rather rich close-harmony sound. As a rule, never over-sing!

3. **Ranges** of individual parts usually allow for the possibility of having a few Tenors, for instance, on the Baritone part, or a few Altos on the 2nd Soprano part, or *vice versa*. This can be useful if you encounter problems with balance or with the numbers of singers available.

Peter Gritton
November 1990

Here, There And Everywhere

Words & Music by John Lennon & Paul McCartney

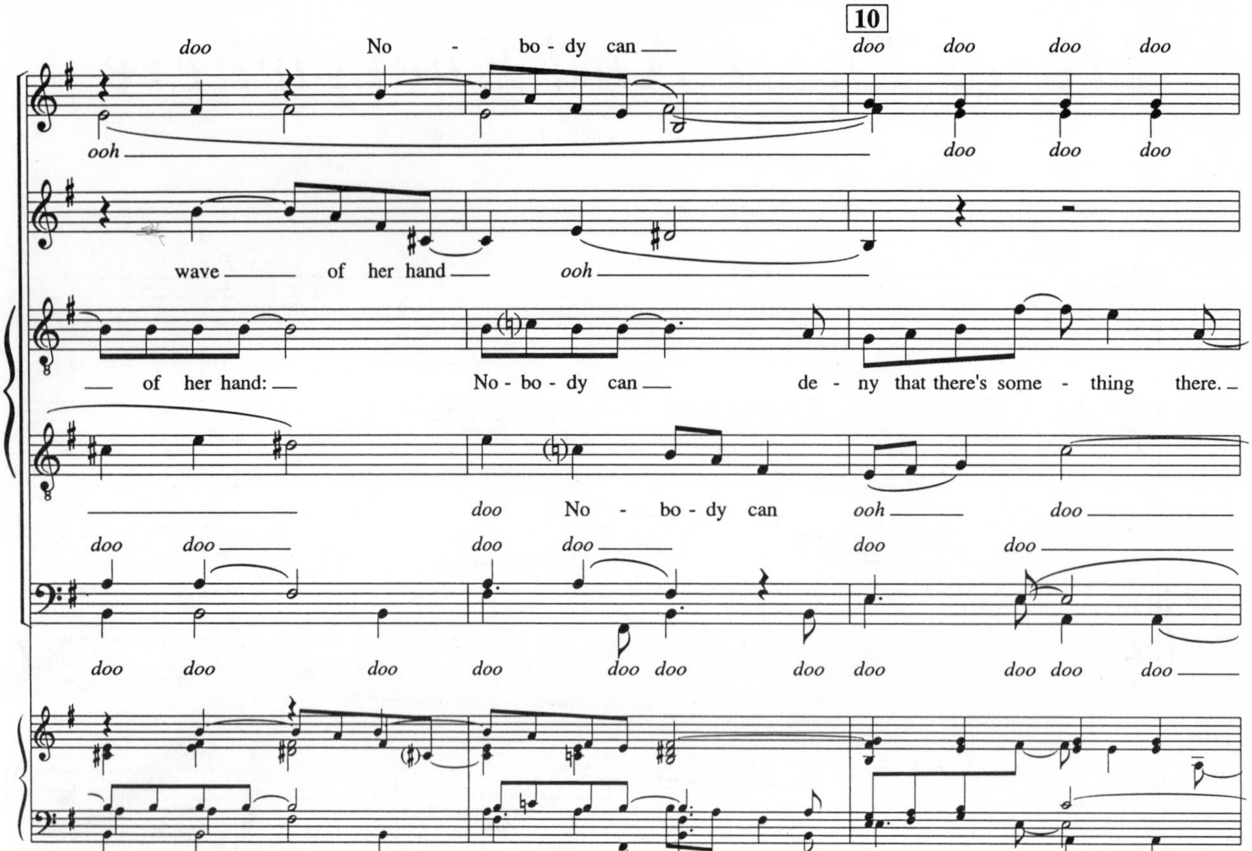

10
doo No - bo - dy can doo doo doo doo
ooh doo doo doo
wave of her hand ooh
of her hand: No - bo - dy can de - ny that there's some - thing there.
doo No - bo - dy can ooh doo
doo doo doo doo doo doo
doo doo doo doo doo doo doo doo doo doo doo

doo doo doo doo doo doo doo doo doo doo doo doo
pp
mm
mf
There, run - ning my hand through her hair,
doo doo
doo doo doo doo doo doo doo doo doo doo
doo doo doo doo doo doo doo doo doo doo

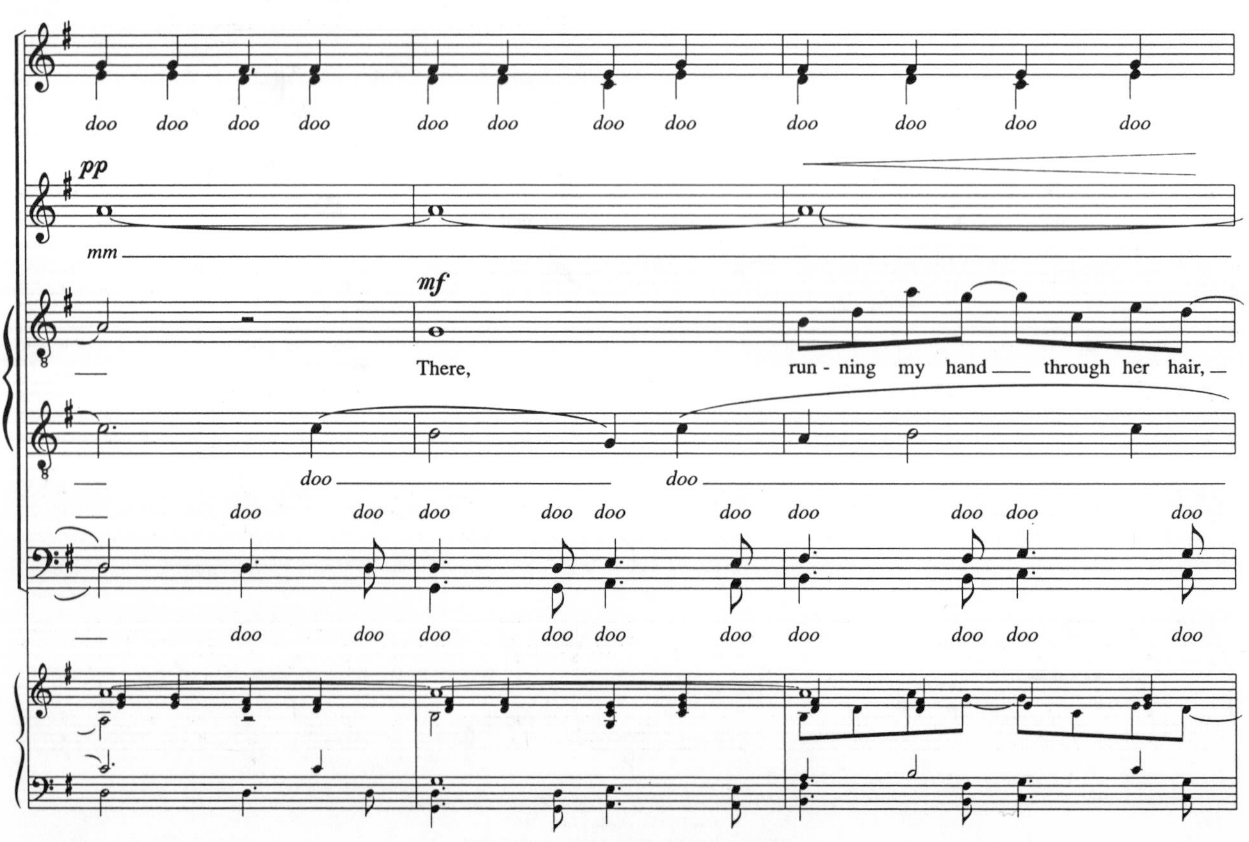

15
mp
doo doo ah
doo doo doo doo doo doo doo doo ooh
(ooh) ah
both of us think - ing how good it can be:
doo doo doo doo doo doo doo
doo doo doo doo doo doo doo doo doo doo doo
doo doo doo doo doo doo doo doo doo doo doo doo
doo doo
doo doo doo doo doo
ooh doo doo doo doo
f
Some - one is speak - ing but she does - n't know he's there. I want her
ooh ooh doo doo I want her
doo doo doo doo doo
doo doo doo doo doo doo doo doo

20
mf ah
S
ah da da
A
mf
ah da da da da da da ne - ver
T
ev' - ry-where and if she's be-side me I know I need ne-ver care.
ev' - ry-where and if she's be-side me I know I need ne-ver care.
B
mf
ah ev' - ry-where da I need ne - ver
mf
ah ev'-ry-where da da da da da
mf
25
p
doo doo doo doo doo doo doo doo
p
care doo doo doo doo doo doo doo to share,
mp
But to love her is to love her ev' - ry - where, know-ing that love is to share,
p
doo doo doo doo doo doo doo doo
p
care mm doo doo doo
port.
p
da mm doo
port.
p

S
A
T
B
ooh
doo
Watch -
doo to share, to share doo doo doo ooh
to share, to share doo doo love ne - ver dies.
each one be - liev - ing that love ne - ver dies,
doo doo doo doo doo doo
doo doo
doo doo doo doo doo doo doo doo doo doo doo
30
- ing her eyes
doo doo
1
doo doo doo doo doo
doo doo doo doo
mf
Watch-ing her eyes and hop - ing I'm al - ways there. I want her
ooh ooh doo doo I want her
doo doo doo doo doo
doo doo doo doo doo doo doo doo

2
S
A
T
B
mp
poco cresc.
doo doo
doo-by-doo wa
doo-by-doo wa
doo doo doo
doo-by-doo doo doo doo doo doo doo
to be there,
doo doo doo Here, there and ev' - ry - where,
doo doo doo doo doo Here, there and ev' - ry -
doo doo doo doo doo doo doo doo doo doo
35
mf
p
doo-by-doo wa ev' - ry - where.
doo-by-doo doo doo doo ev' - ry - where.
Here, there and ev' - ry - where. mm
Here, there and ev' - ry - where. mm
where. Here, there and ev' - ry - where.
doo doo doo doo ev' - ry - where. mm

Hey Jude

Words & Music by John Lennon & Paul McCartney

10
bad, take a sad song and make it bet - ter. Re -
mp
doo doo doo take a sad, sad song and ooh doo doo doo
mp
doo doo doo take a sad song and ooh doo doo
mp
doo doo doo take a sad song and make it and make it bet - ter,
bad, take a sad song and ooh doo
don't make it bad just take a sad, sad song doo doo
- mem - ber to let her in - to your heart, then you can start to make it bet -
mf
doo doo doo ah Hey
doo doo doo doo ah
ah
Re - mem - ber, re - mem - ber, let her in - to your heart, ah
doo doo doo doo ah
doo doo doo doo der doo da da da da
3
mf

15
p
- ter. Hey Jude, Hey Jude you were made to doo
Jude, don't be a - fraid you were made to go out and
p
ooh doo doo doo doo doo Hey Jude, Hey Jude doo doo
ooh
p
ooh Hey Jude doo doo
p
doo doo doo Hey Jude
mp
Hey Jude, don't be a - fraid you were made to
(p)
(mp)
The min - ute you let her un - der your skin, then you be -
get her. The min - ute you let her un - der your skin then you be -
go and get her let her let her you
you let her un - der your skin
go and get her The min - ute you let her un - der your skin you
go and get her you let her let her you
go out and get her da da da da da da da da
mf
3

20
mf dolce
S
- gin to make it bet - ter
And a - ny time you feel the
doo
sf da
mp dolce
A
be - gin to doo ba da da Hey
you be - gin to make it bet - ter ba da da
T
be - gin to make it bet - ter da da
mp dolce
sf
B
be - gin to doo make it bet - ter da da Hey
sf
you be - gin to make it bet - ter bet - ter ba da da da da da da
ritmico
mf dolce
sf
Hey, don't car - ry the world
25
up - on your shoul -
pain,
Hey, don't car - ry the world up - on your
Jude Hey Jude re - frain, re - frain, doo
mf dolce
p
Hey Jude re - frain doo doo doo doo
p
Jude ooh doo doo re - frain doo doo doo doo doo
p
da da da da da doo doo doo doo

S
A
T
B
f
molto
- ders.
For now you know that it's a fool who plays it
shoul - ders.
For now you know who plays it
mf
doo doo 'n' doo da
ba da who plays it
doo doo
doo doo 'n' doo - doo da
ba da who plays it cool,
doo doo doo 'n' doo da
ba da da
doo doo'n' doo da
ba da da da
30
poco lento e sostenuto
cool,
Hey Jude, don't let me
pp
cool, mak - ing his world a lit - tle cold - er, don't let me down, you have
ooh
doo doo
ooh doo doo doo doo doo doo doo doo doo doo doo doo
doo doo doo doo doo doo doo don't let me down,
ooh doo doo doo doo doo doo Hey Jude ooh doo doo
ooh doo doo doo doo doo doo doo doo doo doo doo doo doo

35
piu lento
mp
tranquillo
found her, now go and get her. Re-mem-ber to let her in-to your heart, then you can
doo
mp
— doo doo doo Re - mem - ber in your heart
you have found her now go and get her. Let her in your heart,
p
you have found her, get her. Re-mem-ber in your heart,
— doo doo doo go and get her, let her in your heart.
doo doo doo doo get her, let her in your heart,
piu lento
poco
tranquillo
(poco meno mosso)
40
S
pp
start to make it bet - ter. ooh
A
tranquillo
bet - ter.
pp ooh
start to make it (ooh) bet - ter. ooh.
start, then you can start to make it ooh bet - ter.
T
tranquillo
pp
start, start to make it ooh.
B
tranquillo
pp
start to make it ooh make it ooh (mm)
(poco meno mosso)
pp

It's Only Love

Words & Music by John Lennon & Paul McCartney

* This piece may be sung a semitone lower (in D major).

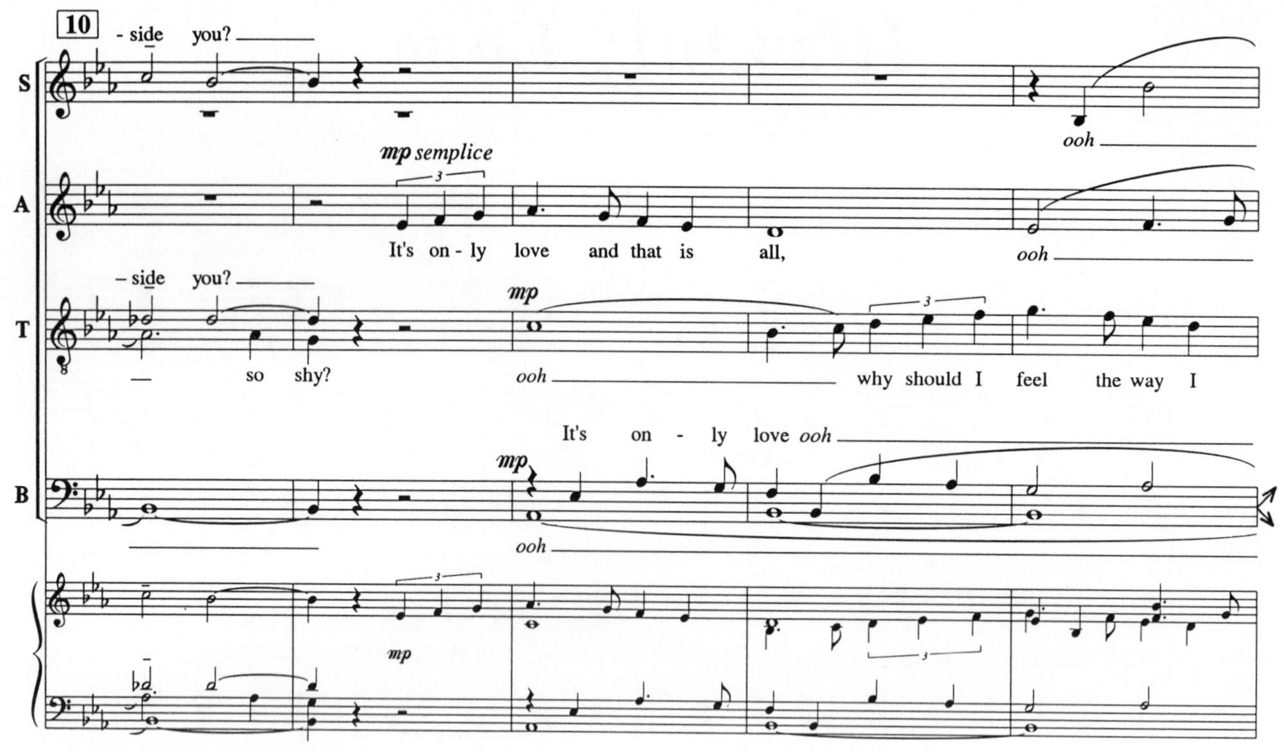

10
S
A
T
B
- side you?
ooh
mp semplice
It's on - ly love and that is all,
ooh
- side you?
mp
— so shy?
ooh
why should I feel the way I
It's on - ly love ooh
mp
ooh
mp

15
S
A
T
B
ah
ooh
mf
— it's — on - ly love
ah
it's so hard, it's so hard
ooh
mf
— ah that's all, but it's so hard lov - ing you.
mf
do? It's — on - ly love and that is all, but it's so hard
ooh
mf
mp
— ah ooh lov - ing you.
mf
mp
— ah ooh lov - ing you.
mf

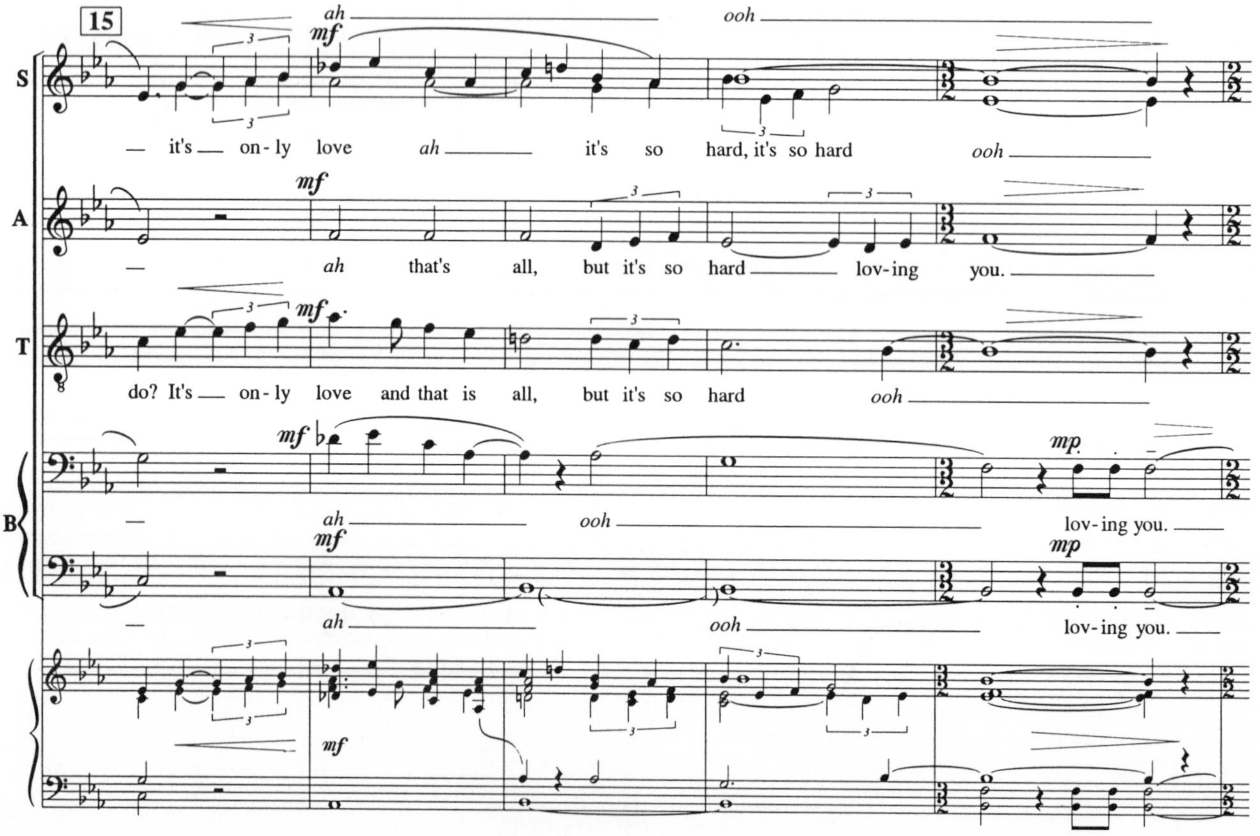

20
mp ma intenso
Is it right that you and I should fight?
Just the sight of
mp ma intenso
Is it right that you and I should fight?
Just the sight of
mp ma intenso
Is it right that you and I should fight?
Just the sight of
p
cresc.
ooh
ooh
mf
ev'-ry night?
mp
mf

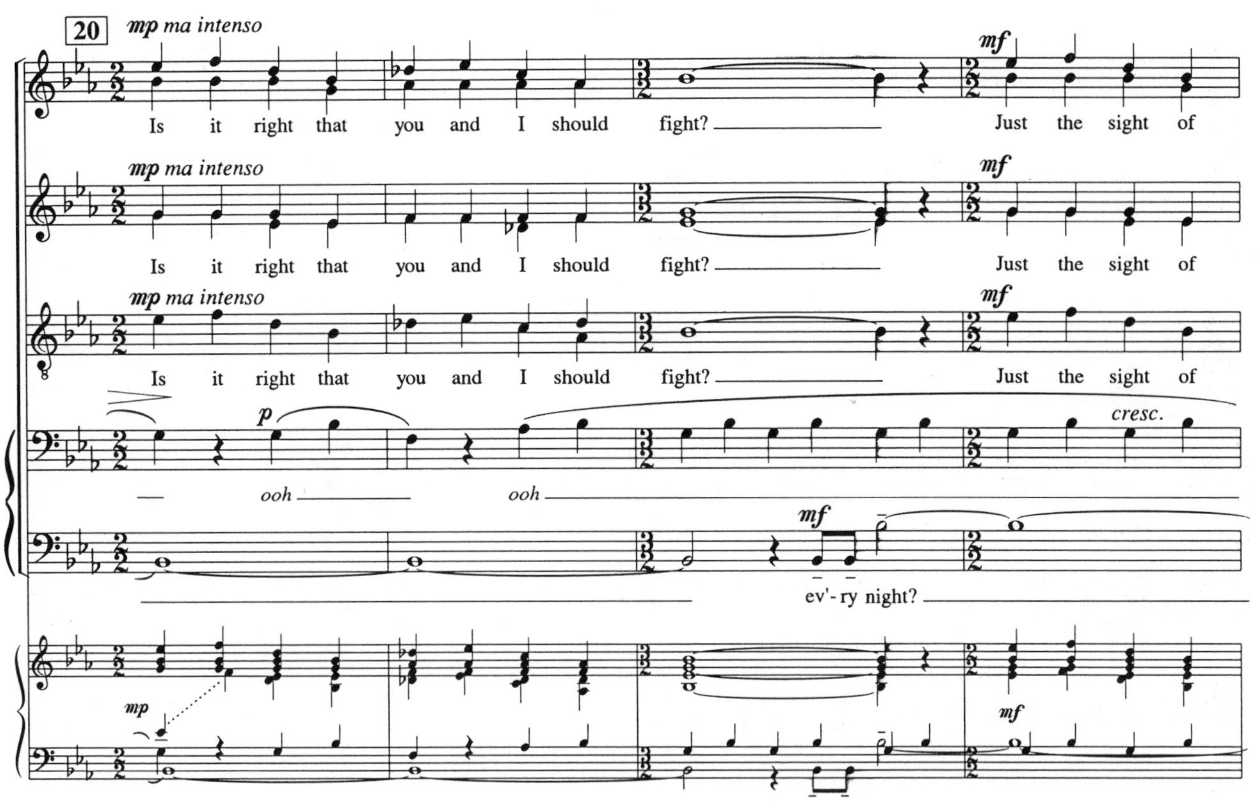

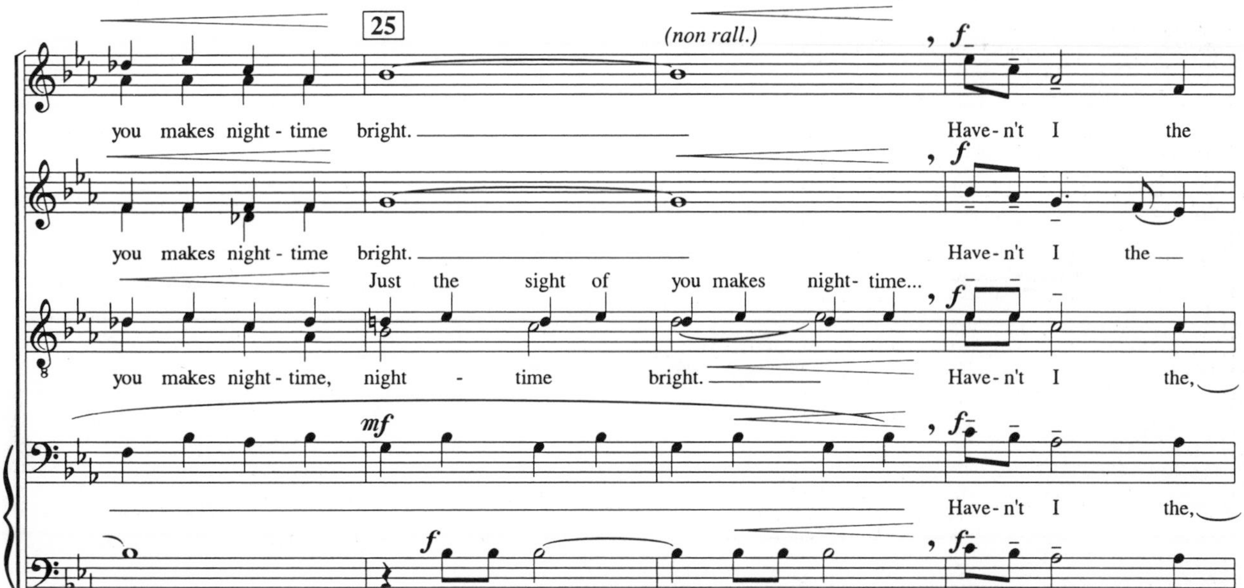

25
(non rall.)
f
you makes night-time bright.
Have-n't I the
f
you makes night-time bright.
Have-n't I the
Just the sight of you makes night-time...
f
you makes night-time, night - time bright.
Have-n't I the,
mf
f
Have-n't I the,
f
f
ve - ry bright, ve - ry bright.
Have-n't I the,
(non rall.)
f

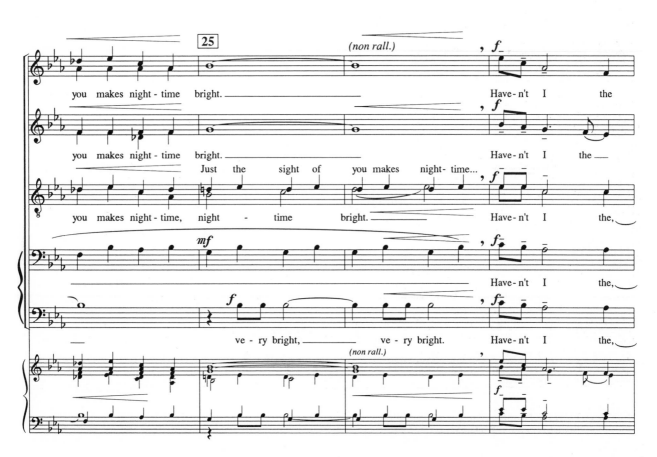

* *original is 'girl', and may be used by authenticists or all-male choirs.*

S *mp* all, but it's so hard, but it's so hard,

A *mf* hard loving you, hard loving

so hard

T it's only love, hard so

B ooh love ooh

but it's so hard

40

S but it's so hard, but it's so hard.

A *p* *mf* you hard loving you, so hard, hard loving you

hard loving

T *p* *mf* hard it's so hard, hard loving, loving

B loving you so

loving you but it's so

p *mf*

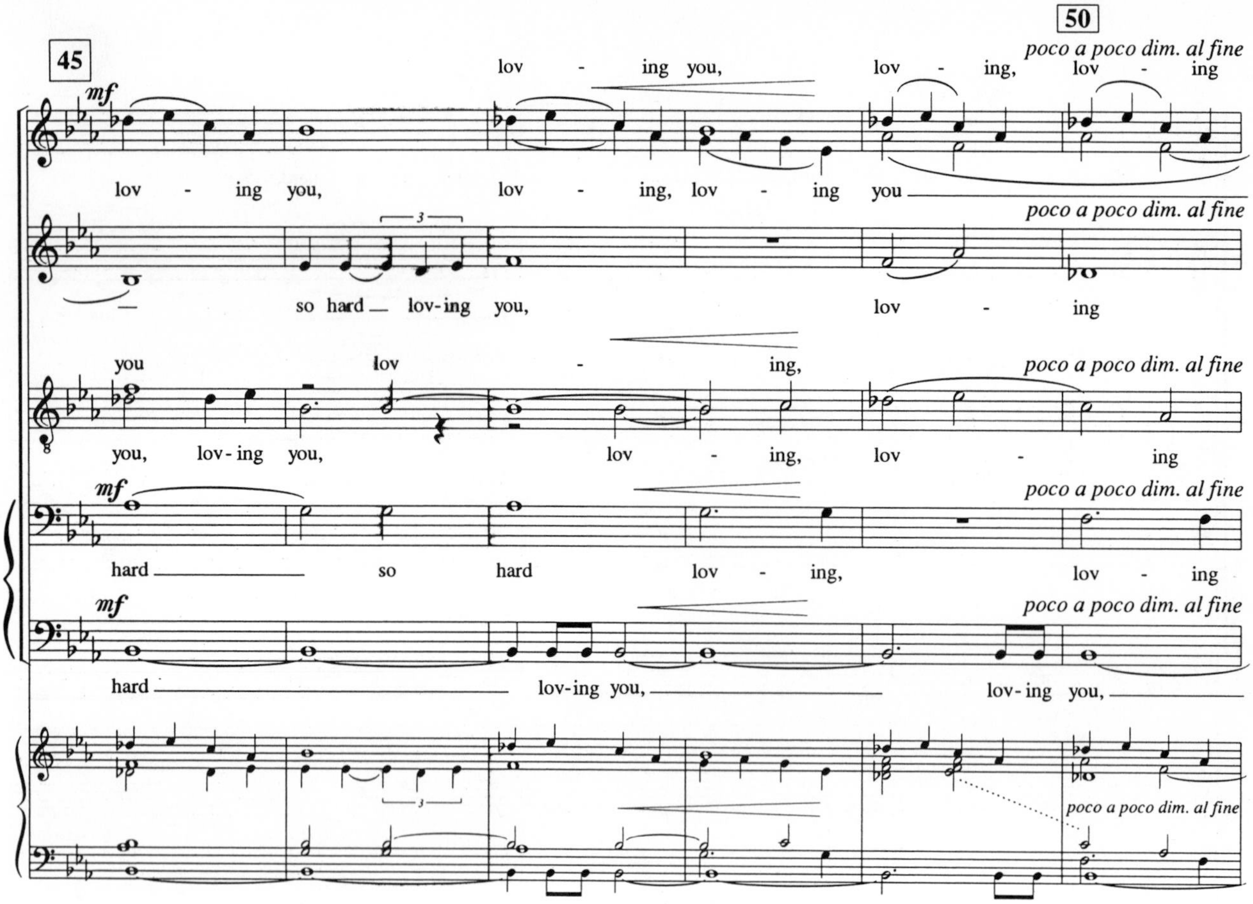

45

50

poco a poco dim. al fine

lov - ing you, lov - ing, lov - ing

mf

lov - ing you, lov - ing, lov - ing you ___

poco a poco dim. al fine

— so hard — lov-ing you, lov - ing

you lov - ing,

poco a poco dim. al fine

you, lov-ing you, lov - ing, lov - ing

mf

poco a poco dim. al fine

hard ___ so hard lov - ing, lov - ing

mf

poco a poco dim. al fine

hard ___ lov-ing you, ___ lov-ing you, ___

poco a poco dim. al fine

Michelle

Words & Music by John Lennon & Paul McCartney

10
S
A
T
B
go to - ge - ther well, my Mi - chelle.
go to - ge - ther well, my Mi - chelle, Oh my Mi - chelle.
go to - ge - ther loo loo loo loo loo loo my Mi - chelle
loo loo loo loo loo loo loo loo loo loo loo I love
loo loo loo loo loo loo loo loo loo loo loo I love you, I love you, I
loo loo loo loo loo loo loo loo loo I love
loo loo loo loo loo loo loo loo loo
15
sans pressant
ah ooh ooh
ah ooh all I want to say ooh
ooh love you
you, love you un - til I find a
love you ooh love you
you That's all I want to say, ooh
love you, love, love you, love
p subito
sans pressant

20
pp tendrement
I will say the on - ly words I know that you'll un - der -
pp
way
ah
ah
Oh
pp
ah
Oh
pp
loo loo
loo loo
loo loo
pp
you,
loo loo
loo loo
loo loo
pp tendrement
25
mf doux
- stand.
Mi - chelle, ma belle, sont les mots qui
Oh
mf doux
Oh
Mi - chelle, ma belle, sont les mots qui
mf doux
Mi - chelle, ma belle, sont les mots qui
mf doux
Mi - chelle, ma belle, sont les mots qui
mf doux
Oh
Mi - chelle, ma belle sont les
mf doux
Mi-chelle, Mi-chelle, Mi-chelle, ma belle, Mi-chelle, sont les mots sont les
mf doux

augmentez un peu
vont très bien en - semble, très bien en - semble. I need you, I need you, I
vont très bien en - semble, très bien en - semble. I need you, I need you, I,
vont très bien en - semble, très bien en- semble. I need you, I need you, I
vont très bien en - semble, très bien en- semble. I need you, I need you, I
mots qui vont très bien en - semble.
mots qui vont très bien, très bien, très bien en- semble.
augmentez un peu
30
need you, I need to make you see Oh what you mean to
I need, I need you, I need to make you see.
need you, I need to make you see, mean to
need you, I need to make you see Oh what you mean, you
I need, I need to make you see what you mean to
I need to make you see

35
en calmant
mp
rit.
me, Un - til I do I'm ho - ping you will know what I mean Oh my Mi -
mp
ooh un - til I do I'm ho - ping you will know what I mean
p
me, you will know what I mean Oh my Mi -
mean to me,
me,
p
dm
en calmant
mp
rit.
p
40
plus lent
ah
p expressif
- chelle.
ah
p expressif
ah
ah
p expressif
- chelle.
ah
ah
p expressif
ah
ah
da
Oh Mi-chelle,
p expressif
ah
ah
p expressif
dm
da
da
da
da
da
da
da
plus lent
p expressif

45

ah long

ah long

ah long

Oh my Mi - chelle, ah Mi - chelle, my Mi - chelle, long

Mi - chelle, Mi - chelle, my Mi - chelle, long

Oh my Mi - chelle, my Mi - chelle, my Mi - chelle, long

Oh my Mi - chelle, my Mi - chelle, long

cresc. *mf* long

Très lent mais flexible (♩.=52)

50

S

A *pp* *poco cresc.* *p*

loo loo loo loo loo loo loo loo loo loo loo loo loo loo mm

T *pp* *poco cresc.* *p*

loo loo loo loo loo loo loo loo loo loo loo loo loo

B *pp* (Solo/Bass I) [Solo]

mm dm dm dm dm doo (mm)

pp *p*

mm dm doo (mm)

Très lent mais flexible (♩.=52)

pp *p*

55

pp

Mi - chelle.

pp

mm

Mi - chelle.

pp

mm

Mi - chelle.

(Solo)

- stand, my Mi - chelle.

Mi - chelle.

(Tutti) pp

mm

mm

pp

Penny Lane

Words & Music by John Lennon & Paul McCartney

10
— stop and say — hel- lo. — And on the cor- ner is a bank-er with a
peo - ple that say hel- lo — bom bom bom
peo - ple that say hel- lo. — bom bom bom
peo - ple that say hel- lo. — bom
mp
On the cor- ner is a
bom peo - ple that say hel- lo. — Oh hel- lo — bom bom bom bom bom

mo - tor car, The lit - tle chil - dren laugh at him be - hind his back, And the
mp
bom The lit - le chil - dren they laugh at him be - hind his back, And
mp
bom bom all the lit - tle chil - dren be - hind his back, be - hind
bank - er with a mo - tor car der da all the chil - dren they laugh at him be - hind his
bom ber bom bom bom bom bom bom

15
bank-er ne-ver wears a mac in the pour-ing rain, ve-ry strange; Pen-ny Lane
bom bom bom bom bom no mac doo 'n' doo doo ba
bom bom bom bom bom no mac doo doo doo ba
back, bom bom bom bom no mac doo doo doo ba
bom bom bom bom no mac doo doo doo ba

20
is in my ears and in my eyes.
ah
and in my, in my eyes ah
Pen-ny Lane in my ears
and in my, in my eyes ah
ba ba ba ba ba ba ba ba
and in my, in my eyes ah
ba ba ba ba ba ba ba ba
and in my, in my eyes my eyes

S
A
T
B
There be-neath the blue sub-ur-ban skies
Full of fish and fin-ger pies
ooh doo doo ah
I sit and
in sum - mer
ooh doo doo doo doo ah
ooh doo doo doo doo doo doo ah
ooh doo doo doo doo doo doo doo
I sit and
in sum - mer,
doo doo doo doo doo
der der der der der der der der der der der der
25
bom bom bom bom bom
mean - while back in Pen-ny Lane there is a fire-man with an hour - glass, And in his
mean - while Back be-hind the shel-ter in the mid-dle of the round-a-bout, A pret-ty
In Pen-ny Lane there is a fire-man with an hour - glass,
Be-hind the shel-ter in the mid-dle of the round-a-bout
back in bom bom bom bom
mean - while back in
mean - while back in
bom bom bom bom
der da da bom bom bom bom bom

30

S
bom *bom* *bom* He likes to keep his
She feels as if she's

A
pock - et is a por - trait of the Queen. He likes to keep his fire - en - gine clean; —
nurse is sell - ing pop - pies from a tray. And though she feels as if she's in a play, —

T
bom *bom* *bom* *bom* He he likes to keep his en - gine,
she feels as if she's in a,

And in his pock - et of — the Queen. He likes to keep his
is sell - ing pop - pies from — a tray. She feels as if she's

B
bom *bom* *bom* *bom* He likes to keep his
She feels as if she's

---

f

en - gine clean, his en - gine clean } in Pen - ny, Pen - ny Lane —
in a play, she's in a play

mf

— it's a clean — ma - chine. } In Pen - ny —
— she is a - ny - way.

mf

his en - gine clean, — his en - gine — clean — } in Pen - ny Lane
she's in a play. — She's in a — play —

mf

en - gine clean, his en - gine, en - gine — clean — } in Pen - ny Lane
in a play, she's in a, in a — play —

en - gine clean, his en - gine clean in } *doo* Pen - ny Lane — *doo der*
in a play, she's in a play in

mf

35

— is in my ears — and in my eyes. —

Lane — is in — my — in my eyes — *ah*

Pen-ny Lane — in my ears — is in — my — in my eyes — *ah*

Pen-ny Lane — in my ears — is in — my — in my eyes — *ah*

is in — my — in my eyes — *ah*

ba ba ba ba ba ba ba ba is in — my — in — my eyes, — my eyes.

40

S: There be-neath the blue — sub-ur-ban skies. — *mp* Back in Pen-ny

A: *ooh doo doo doo* — *p sub.* Back in

T: *ooh doo doo doo* — *ah* — *p sub.* Back in

B: *ooh doo doo doo* — *doo doo doo* — *f* I sit and mean-while back in *p sub.*

doo doo doo doo doo derderderderderderderderderderderder *fp* *der doo da* — *bom*

f *p*

45
mf
Lane the bar- ber shaves a - no- ther cus- to- mer, We see the bank- er sit- ting wait- ing for a trim, And then the
bom bom bom bom bom bom – ting, And then the
bom bom bom bom bom bom – ting for, and then the
bom bom bom bom the bank- er sit- ting wait - ing for a
bom bom bom bom bom bom – ting for a trim bom

fire- man rush - es in from the pour - ing rain,
fire- man rush '- es in from the pour - ing rain,
(like a siren)
fire- man rush - es ee na nee na ooh nee na
f
noo noo noo noo noo noo noo noo noo noo noo noo noo noo noo noo noo noo noo noo noo noo noo noo
noo noo noo noo noo noo noo noo noo noo noo noo noo noo noo noo noo Pen - ny

50
S
A
B
Pen - ny Lane, Pen - ny Lane
ve - ry strange; ooh Pen - ny Lane is in my ears and in my eyes,
ooh Pen - ny Lane is in my ears and in my
Pen - ny Lane, Pen - ny Lane is in my ears and in my

oh Pen - ny, Pen - ny Lane
Pen - ny Lane, Pen - ny Lane is in my ears
eyes, Pen - ny Lane's in me Pen - ny Lane is
Pen - ny Lane's in me
eyes, Pen - ny, Pen - ny Lane, oh Pen - ny Lane is

55

poco a poco tranquillo

S: *dim. poco a poco*
Pen - ny Lane, Pen - ny Lane

A: *dim. poco a poco*
and in my eyes.

T: *dim. poco a poco*
in my ears and eyes, in my eyes.

dim. poco a poco
In my ears and eyes, in my eyes, ears and eyes.

dim. poco a poco
in my ears and eyes, in my ears and eyes.

B:
in my ears and eyes, in my eyes.
dim. poco a poco

poco a poco tranquillo
dim. poco a poco

60

Poco meno mosso al fine

p *mp* Pen -
ooh Pen - ny,

p
ooh

mp
Pen - ny Lane is in my ears and in my eyes.

p
ooh Pen - ny,

ooh
p
ooh (mm)

Poco meno mosso al fine
mp
p

65
S
A
T
B
mp
- ny, Pen - ny, Pen - ny, Pen - ny,
ooh Pen - ny,
Pen - ny, ooh
There be-neath the blue sub-ur - ban skies,
Pen - ny, Pen - ny, ooh
ooh
poco rit.
70
Pen - ny Lane.
Pen - ny, Pen - ny Lane.
Pen - ny Lane.
Pen - ny Lane.
Pen - ny Lane
Pen - ny Lane.
Pen - ny Lane.

With A Little Help From My Friends

Words & Music by John Lennon & Paul McCartney

* ♫ and ♪. ♬ = ♩ ♪ (triplet)

** The tune has been omitted from the reduction for practical purposes.

wap wap doo wap doo doo doo wa
wap wap doo wap doo doo doo wa
wap wap doo wap doo doo doo wa
[v.2 solo]
[v.2 Tutti]
Lend me your ears and I'll sing you a song, and I'll try not to sing out of key.
How do I feel by the end of the day? Are you sad because you're on your own?
doo doo doo doo doo doo doo doo doo ba doo doo doo

10
mf
1. Oh I get by with a lit-tle help from my friends, Ah I get high
2. No
mf
1. Oh I get by, help, my friends, Ah I get high,
2. No
ooh help, my friends, from my friends,
doo ba doo doo doo doo doo doo doo doo doo
mf

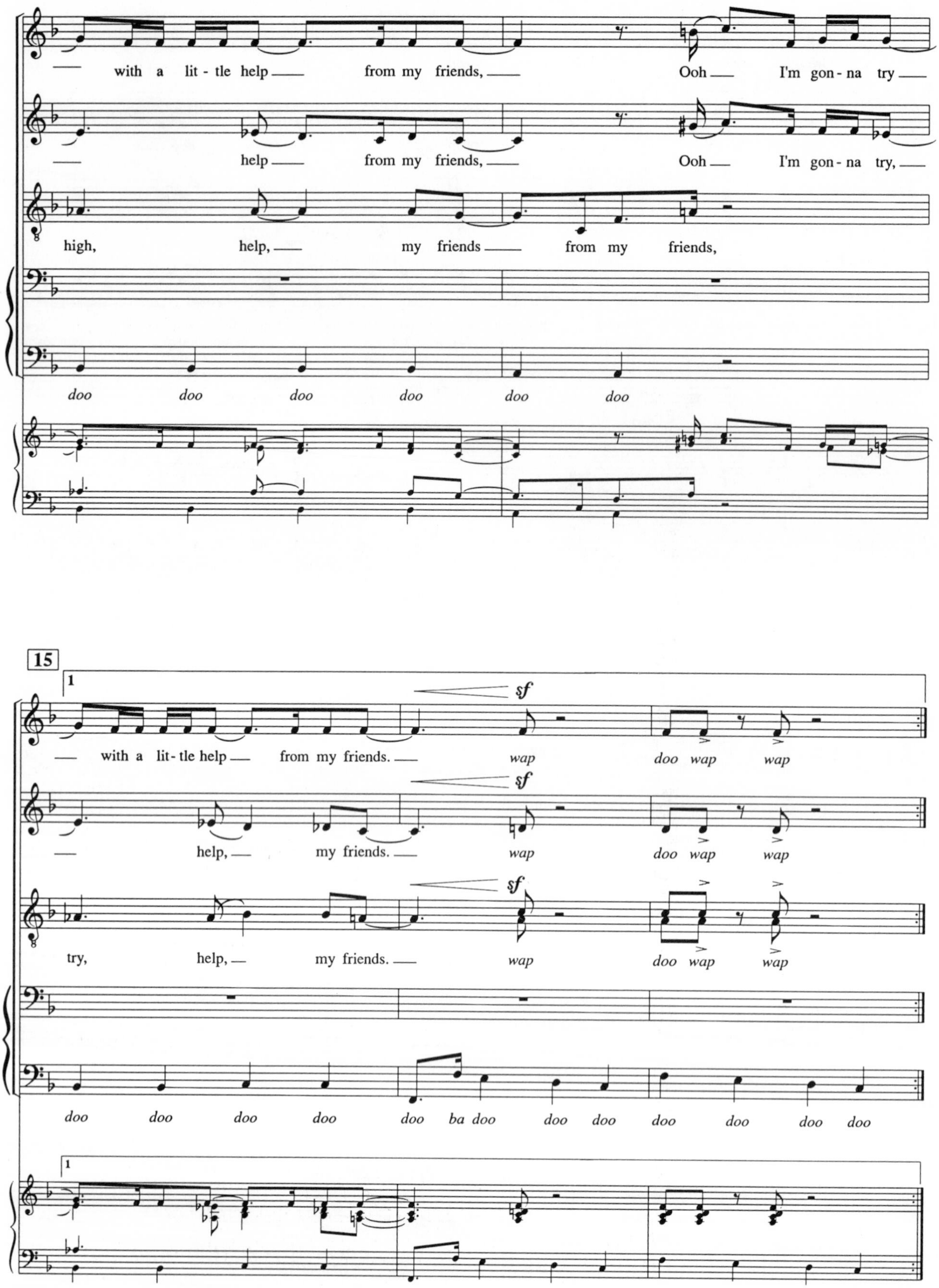

15

1

sf

with a lit - tle help from my friends. *wap* *doo wap* *wap*

help, my friends. *wap* *doo wap* *wap*

try, help, my friends. *wap* *doo wap* *wap*

doo doo doo doo doo ba doo doo doo doo doo doo doo

1

2
20
f
with a lit-tle help from my friends. Do you need any - bo -
help, my friends. Do you need a - ny - bo -
try, help, my friends. Do you need a - ny - bo -
Do you need a - ny - bo -
(più marcato)
doo doo doo doo doo doo doo doo doo doo doo doo ba dm dm doo

mp
f
- dy? I need some - bo - dy to love. Could it be
- dy? I need some - bo - dy to love. Could it be
- dy? I need some - bo - dy to love. Could it be
- dy? to love. Could it be
dm dm dm doo dm dm dm dm dm dm dm dm

sf 25 mp

a - ny - bo - dy? I want some - bo - dy to love,

a - ny - bo - dy? I want som - bo - dy to love,

a - ny - bo - dy? I want som - bo - dy to love,

a - ny - bo - dy? to love,

(più legato)

doo doo doo doo doo doo doo ba doo dm dm doo doo ba doo doo doo

pp ritmico (vibrato) 30 p

Some - one to love. doo

Some - one to love. doo

Some - one to love. doo

Some - one to love. Would you be - lieve in a love -

doo doo doo doo doo doo doo doo doo doo doo doo doo doo doo doo

35

slow

doo — wap I can't tell — you but I know — it's mine. —

doo — wap I can't tell — you but I know — it's mine. —

doo — wap I can't tell — you but I know — it's mine. —

What would you see — when you turn — out the light?

doo doo doo doo doo doo doo doo doo doo doo doo

pp
(,)
(,)
mm
mm
mm
mm
mm
doo
Mm I get by with a lit-te help from my friends,
Mm I get high
doo ba doo mm
mm
dm
doo ba doo mm
doo

40
(,)
(,)
doo
doo
mm
doo
with a lit - tle help from my friends,
Mm I'm gon - na
dm
doo ba doo mm
doo

(,)
(,)
f
help, my friends. Do you need a - ny - bo -
help, my friends. Do you need a - ny - bo -
help, my friends. Do you need a - ny - bo -
try with a lit- tle help from my friends. Do you need a - ny - bo -
help, doo doo doo doo doo doo doo doo doo ba dm dm doo

45
p
f
- dy? I just need some - one to love. Could it be
- dy? I just need some - one to love. Could it be
- dy? I just need some - one to love. Could it be
- dy? to love. Could it be
dm dm dm doo doo ba doo doo doo doo doo doo doo

50
a - ny - bo - dy? I just need some - one to
a - ny - bo - dy? I just need some - one to
a - ny - bo - dy? I just need some - one to
a - ny - bo - dy? I just need some - one to
doo doo doo doo doo doo doo ba doo dm dm doo doo need some - one to

sempre dim.
love. mm I get by with a lit - tle help from my friends,
sempre dim.
love. mm I get by, help my friends,
love. ooh
love, love, love ooh ooh I get by, help my friends,
mp
love. I want some - bo - dy to love, I
mp
doo dm der doo dm der dm dm dm dm dm dm dm dm

CHORAL CONNECTION

With A Little Help From My Friends

6 Beatles songs in close harmony

S.A.T.B.

Editor: Peter Gritton

CHESTER MUSIC

55
sempre cresc.
get by with a lit-tle help from my friends, get high
sempre cresc.
get by, help from my friends, get high
sempre cresc.
get by, help, my friends, get high
mf sempre cresc.
want some - bo - dy to love, Ah I get high
sempre cresc.
dm dm dm dm dm dm dm dm dm dm dm dm
60
ff dolce
(long)
with a lit-tle help from my friends,
ff dolce
1. (long)
2. (long)
with a litt-tle help from my friends.
from my friends.
ff dolce
2. (long)
1. (long)
with a lit-tle help from my friends, my friends.
ff dolce
(long)
with a lit-tle help from my friends, from my friends.
ff
(long)
doo doo doo doo da da da da da da from my friends.
(long)
ff
dolce
(long)